Gowk the Cuckoo
Call of the Spring

Text © John Miles
Illustrations © Barry Robson

Langford Press, 10 New Road,
Langtoft, Peterborough, PE6 9LE
www.langford-press.co.uk

A CIP Record for this book is
available from the British Library
ISBN 978-1-904078-65-4

Designed by MRM Graphics Ltd
Printed in Spain under the supervision
of MRM Graphics Ltd, Winslow

Broads Authority
The Broads - a member of the
National Park family

Gowk the Cuckoo sponsored by Broads Authority,
and CleySpy

Gowk the Cuckoo

by John Miles
and
artwork by Barry Robson

Myweebooks

Langford Press

Gowk the Cuckoo

What a journey! Gowk has come all the way from Africa and is now crossing the English Channel. He has already done more than 7,000 miles (11,000 kilometres). Just a few more to go and he will be back in England. Those tired wings which have carried him all that way now need a rest, so he stops off on a cross channel ferry to catch his breath.
Fortunately, he picks one going the right way or he could have ended up back at Calais in France! The white cliffs are getting closer, so he decides

to fly the last mile to land and on into Kent. No more sea crossings for him; he flies on through London and on to Norfolk. This is his first flight back to where he was born after being dumped into a reed warblers' nest as an egg and reared by these little birds. Then he had to fly to Africa on his own, thinking about where he should go for the winter. He has never met his real parents, although he has seen other cuckoos in the forests of West Africa.

5

This is an exciting time
for Gowk as he is full of
the joys of spring.
The first place he stops is
a reed bed at Strumpshaw
Fen. This is part of a big
marshy area, or wetland,
called the Norfolk Broads.
It is just outside a big
city called Norwich with
its tall cathedral and a
famous pair of peregrine
falcons. Gowk does not
want to meet them, as he
would end up with no more
flights to Africa!

ROBSON '14

Strumpshaw provides him with his first big meal of caterpillars, his favourite food.

He particularly likes the hairy ones and the many-coloured ones, which other birds cannot eat.

Many of these caterpillars are poisonous, but Gowk has a cast-iron stomach and can squeeze out the poison before eating them. One of these brightly coloured caterpillars will change into the rare swallowtail butterfly.

Like many butterflies, swallowtails lay lots of eggs.

They hatch out into caterpillars and many of them are eaten.

The caterpillars that survive become the next generation of butterflies.

9

Gowk was a cuckoo, and the spring sunshine makes him sing out his name over and over again. It was the French who gave him his English name today as the spelling of 'coucou' ended up as 'cuckoo' in English. The name 'Gowk' comes from the Norse word for the cuckoo. It has something to do with the fact that the cuckoo plays a game of trying to look like a bird of prey called the sparrowhawk. Males and females like Gowk have blue-grey backs and there is a rare brown female cuckoo just like the female sparrowhawk.

Small birds chase and shout at the cuckoo as if it is a bird of prey. When a female cuckoo approaches a reed warbler's nest, the warbler leaves the nest to protect itself. It stays away long enough for the female cuckoo to lay an egg in the nest. Gowk sings to find a female to mate with, so that these eggs are fertile (will hatch out). Cuckoos need to find several reed warbler nests to complete a clutch of eggs, which is spread around, one in each nest. Gowk is early this year and cuckoo females have not arrived yet, so he decides to move around the Broads to look for mates.

This amazing area of the Norfolk Broads covers 117 square miles (303 square kilometres) of reed beds, lakes, wet woodland and rivers, as well as wet marshy fields where cows can graze. The open areas of water were once peat beds, created by all the dead plants being squashed together over thousands of years and never rotting away. The Romans dug the peat

to burn for heating their houses. All this digging went on into the Middle Ages. Once the digging stopped, water soon filled the large holes left behind, making the 'broad' areas of water you see today.

Gowk is bound to find some females here! He tries his luck around the largest area of open water and reed bed at Hickling Broad.

Gowk keeps singing 'cuckoo' from dawn till dusk. Finally he is lucky and a female, shouting her bubbling call, joins him so she can lay fertile eggs. She finds a reed warbler nest and takes out an egg, so that they do not guess there is any change in the nest. Her own egg looks almost exactly the same, just slightly larger. The cuckoo chick hatches after 11 to 13 days, sooner than the reed warblers, and the first job is to push the remaining warbler eggs out of the nest. This is to make sure this cuckoo chick will get all the food that a whole brood of reed warbler chicks would normally eat. The cuckoo chick can even make enough noise to make the poor warblers think there is a whole family wanting to be fed, so the new parents bring plenty of food. The chick also has bright colours inside its mouth, or gape. The warblers can't resist stuffing more and more food into this big, colourful mouth. The chick leaves the nest after another 17 to 21 days, depending on how much food the warblers can find. Then it is the cuckoo's turn to chase the parent birds for food, calling as it goes.

ROBSON '14

Gowk can have several females as partners and decides to explore new areas. This time he goes north along the Norfolk coast to Cley, where a large reed bed, with birdwatching hides, catches his eye. There are many people here with binoculars and telescopes watching all the birds from the hides, so as not to disturb them.
There are many caterpillars on the willow trees and reeds, so Gowk does not go hungry, and also there are several females to keep him company.

The urge to head south is never too far from Gowk's mind. Some cuckoos stay only six weeks in Britain before flying off again. Gowk has a trip to the Norfolk Brecklands, at Weeting Heath, which birdwatchers know all about because rare stone curlews nest there. This is a sandy area with gorse bushes and grass kept short by nibbling rabbits. There are plenty of caterpillars and grasshoppers, ideal food for Gowk who needs to put on weight ready for his migration to Africa.

18

By the time he has made the long flight back, he will be quite thin again. More than 800 kinds of moths have been recorded at Weeting, and many of them produce lots of caterpillars. Female cuckoos here lay their eggs in the nests of meadow pipits, just like most of the cuckoos in open moorland areas around Britain, where the meadow pipit is very common. Reed warblers are not found here, as reeds do not grow in this type of habitat.

Gowk is soon flying back over the English Channel - no ferry needed this time - and across France towards the Alps. Past generations of cuckoos may well have seen the general, Hannibal, heading towards this mountain range in 218 BC, with his army and a troop of elephants, ready to attack the Romans on the other side. Like Hannibal, Gowk will have to find a series of valleys to help him cross the mountains, which rise up to 13,000 feet (4,000 metres) on each side. These lower areas would be safer to cross than the rocky, often snowy, peaks and still offer food if he needs it.

Gowk flies into Italy and south to the River Tiber, which has the great city of Rome built by its banks. Here you find the ancient remains of the Roman Empire, such as the Coliseum and the Pantheon.

22

It also is famous for the Vatican, the centre of the Roman Catholic Church. Gowk was not sightseeing but feeding along the river, to help him continue his journey. Cuckoos help the olive growers in Italy by feeding on the pests of the olive trees.

He flies further south to the island of Sicily off the toe of Italy. Here he finds more feeding areas, including the vast mountain of Etna, which is Europe's most active volcano with smoke pouring out of its crater.

Fortunately, he does not have to fly over this mountain so he avoids his wings being singed! He eats more food here, because the next leg of his journey gets even harder.

Gowk crosses the Mediterranean Sea via the island of Malta. This island should be a benefit for cuckoos and all the birds migrating south, as somewhere to rest before the final hop into Africa. Sadly, many people on this beautiful island see birds just as something to shoot at and many cuckoos never continue their migration.

A small band of local people with the help of people from other countries are trying to make the island a better place for birds by encouraging people to come to the island to enjoy its wildlife. They will spend money in the local shops and hotels, which will help the people of Malta, and fewer birds will be killed.

Gowk makes it into Africa, heading across Libya and down into the Sahara Desert via Lake Chad. This lake is a miracle in a sea of sand for birds on migration, not just for its fresh drinking water but also for its large reed beds, marshland and agriculture.

The lake itself was once an inland sea, but has shrunk over 7,000 years.
The water in the lake was reduced by 95% between 1963 and 1998.
Fortunately, for Gowk and the other migrating birds, the lake has
started to rise again, offering more food and shelter.

The final leg takes Gowk into West Africa and the Congo Basin.
Here the tropical forests offer shade from the hot African sun.
Gowk now becomes very much a woodland bird, using the dense forest
to hunt for juicy caterpillars high up in the canopy. The forest has
a huge variety of butterflies and moths, many of which have

caterpillars which are poisonous, giving Gowk the gift of rich pickings. He also has an abundant supply of termites once they take flight from the drier forest floor. For several months this is his new home until the urge to migrate north and the thought of those Norfolk Broads get the better of him!

----- BTO Satellite
      Tagging System

----- Main Migration
      Routes

The British Trust for Ornithology (BTO) started catching cuckoos in 2011 from around Norfolk, adding a satellite tag so that the birds could be studied for the life of the tag. With lots of support from organisations such as the *Broads Authority* and individual sponsors, the scheme now involves catching cuckoos from other areas, some of them in Scotland and in Wales. As a result some amazing new facts have been learnt about the birds. Many of these facts are incorporated in this story.

Follow Gowk on:
http://www.bto.org/science/migration/tracking-studies/cuckoo-tracking/gowk

Present books in the series – *Kitty the Toon and Screamer the Swift*
Forthcoming books – *Mavis the Song Thrush,*
Tony the Tawny Owl, Odessa the Osprey, Glead the Red Kite and many more.

A big 'Thank You' to Cleyspy   *http://www.cleyspy.co.uk/* and to the Broads Authority
http://www.broads authority.gov.uk/
who are both part sponsors of this book.

32